£5.99

Meet the Rugrats

TOMMY
Age: 1
Best Point: Leader of the gang
Worst Point: Fearless and curious, leads the others in over their heads.

ANGELICA
Age: 3
Best Point: Looks sickeningly sweet
Worst Point: A bully

CHUCKIE
Age: 2
Best Point: Very loyal friend
Worst Point: Worry wart

SUZIE
Age: 3
Best Point: Energetic and cheerful
Worst Point: Moody

KIMI
Age: 1 and a half
Best Point: Imagination
Worst Point: Gets carried away with excitement

PHIL & LIL
Age: 15 months
Best Point: The cheerleaders of the group
Worst Point: Love to eat worms!

DIL
Age: 3 months
Best Point: irresistibly cute
Worst Point: Tantrums

Contents

SOON...

HEY, ANGELICA, ARE YOU GETTING ICE CREAM?

YEAH, FOR *ME*! YOU GET ICE CUBES.

HUH?

WE'RE GONNA USE THESE ICE CUBES TO *FREEZE* YOUR HAIR OFF!

THAT DOESN'T SOUND VERY NICE. BBBBBRRRRRR!

WHO *CARES* WHAT YOU THINK?

DOUBLE FUDGE CHIP

A-A-ANGEL-GELICA, A-A-ARE YOU SH-SH-SURE TH-TH-THIS IS GO-GOING TO WO-WORK?

WELL... NOT REALLY, BUT WE'LL SEE!

I--I DON'T TH-TH-THINK THIS IS WOR-WORKING OUT, EITHER.

QUIET! YOU'RE NOT TRYING HARD ENOUGH!

BBBRRRR...

C'MON, CHUCKIE, GIMME THAT HAIR!

CYNTHIA NEEDS IT!

CYNTHIA?

YOU MEAN...

...THERE'S NO RUG MONSTER?

'COURSE NOT! I MADE THAT UP!

OOPS.

The End

11

SPOT THE BALL

Tommy, Chuckie and Phil are each playing with a football.

Can you draw in where you think each football should be?

Answers on page 61

LOST AND FOUND!

13

-GZZLE-
SNRT-

...AND THAT'S HOW THE MASKED DETECTIVE FOILED THE--

TOMMY? CHUCKIE? ANGELICA?

NOW, WHERE DID THOSE SPROUTS WANDER OFF TO?

HMM. THAT SHOULDN'T BE OPEN! BETTER TALK TO STU 'BOUT FIXIN' THOSE OLD HINGES!

WELL, THERE YOU ARE!

SAY, THAT'S QUITE A DISCOVERY YOU'VE MADE THERE!

BUT I THINK IT'S WAY PAST YOUR NAPTIME.

"SAAAAY, WHERE'S ANGELICA?"

COME BACK WITH MY DOLLIES, ANGELICA!

YEAH, THESE WILL FOOL GRANDPA!

WON'T LET THEM NO-GOOD BABIES GET ME IN TROUBLE FOR LOSIN' 'EM!

17

HUH?

WHEW! THE BABIES WERE HERE THE WHOLE TIME!

HEY!

YOU BABIES CHEATED!

WHA--?!

ANGELICA STOLE MY DOLLIES!

UH-OH.

BUT-BUT...THEY CHEATED!

I DON'T WANT TO HEAR IT! I THINK SOMEONE NEEDS A TIME-OUT!

BUT-BUT...I'M THE QUEEN SOUP-REEN OF HIDE-AND-PEEEEEEK!

The End

HANG ON
to your diaper!

Tommy is giving Dil a piggy back ride. Help him find his way through the maze to Spike.

Answer: page 60

SNOW RACE

Who is going to win the race to the snowman?

Answer: page 61

REPTAR'S Code Breaker

Put the initial letters of each person into the answer grid to spell out the message.

Some letters are done for you.

What is Reptar saying?

Write your answer here

Answer: page 61

ANGELICA, WOULD YOU LIKE SOME CANDY? I'VE BEEN SAVING IT FOR A SPECIAL OCCASION.

MMPH, MMM! HEY, THANKS. MMMM, MMMM! GOT ANY MORE?

ER...I THINK SO. LET ME CHECK MY ROOM.

GOBBLE GOBBLE

TAKE YOUR TIME.

HAVING ANGELICA BE MY GIRLFRIEND SURE FEELS A LOT LIKE WHEN WE WEREN'T FRIENDS. EXCEPT NOW I'M NOT SUPPOSED TO KEEP ANY CANDY OR SECRETS FROM HER.

WHEN WE WERE GOING OUT YOU USED TO ALWAYS BRING ME FLOWERS.

OF COURSE!

AND, WHAT? YOU FIGURED I STOPPED ENJOYING FLOWERS BECAUSE WE GOT MARRIED?

ER...WELL, I ALWAYS MEANT TO!

I GUESS THERE'S A LOT MORE TO BEING A GOOD BOYFRIEND I HAVE TO LEARN.

I SURE HOBE ANGELICA LIKES DEEZ.

SPIKE'S WORDSEARCH

Can you help Spike find his favourite words in the puzzle?

Tick off the word from the list when you have found it.

Dog ☐
Bones ☐
Lead ☐
Walk ☐
Dig ☐
Bury ☐
Kennel ☐
Collar ☐
Stick ☐
Tail ☐
Wag ☐
Bark ☐
Spike ☐

C E M Z C O L L A R
C J T Q G O K D M Z
E W K V J A E C D H
T A I L N L N H D E
B A R K D M N F S K
N S X B O N E S T I
B U R Y G E L X I P
W A L K P F L J C S
S N X J D A E L K G
Y H S G G A W D I G

Answers: page 61

WHOSE SHADOW?

Can you guess who this is? Colour in the areas containing one circle and find out! If you don't recognise the shadow, unscramble the letters to work out this Rugrat's name.

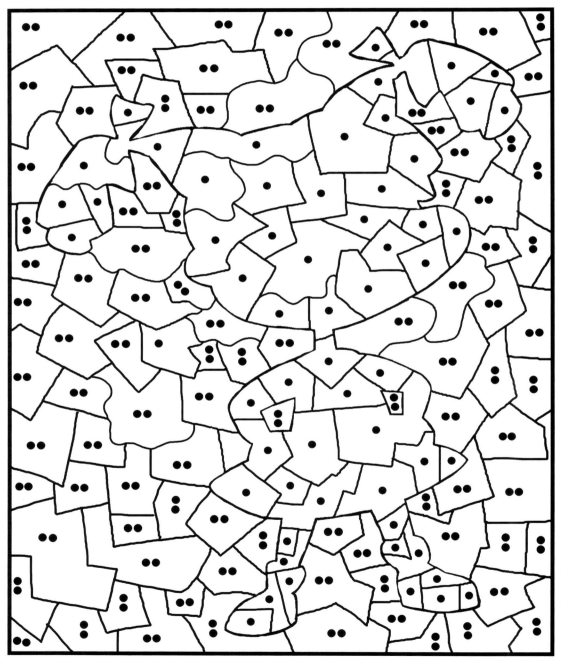

Answer: page 60

L G A E C A N I

AAAAAH!

WHAT'S THE MATTER, CHUCKIE?

THE SKY IS FALLING! THE SKY IS FALLING!

WHAT?

I-I-I COULDN'T SLEEP AND I OPENEDED MY EYES-- A-AND THERE THEY WERE F-FALLING DOWN ON US...!

~GASP!~ LOOK! OUTSIDE SPACE IS INSIDE TOMMY'S ROOM!

RELAX, YOU GUYS. MY MOMMY AND DADDY PUT THOSE THERE.

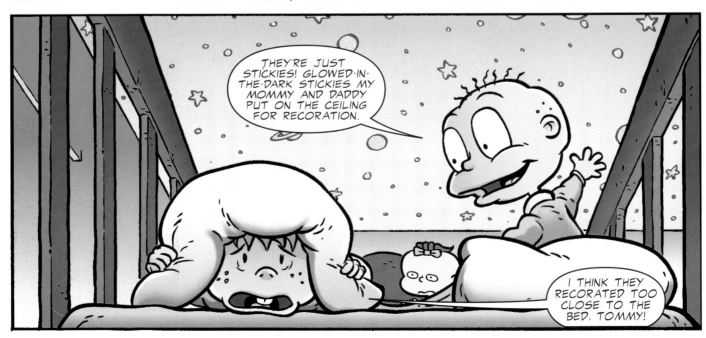

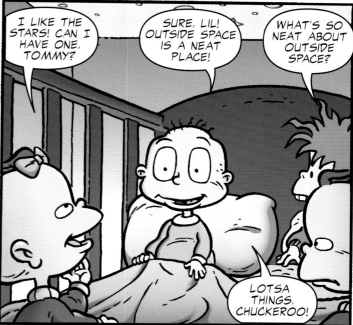

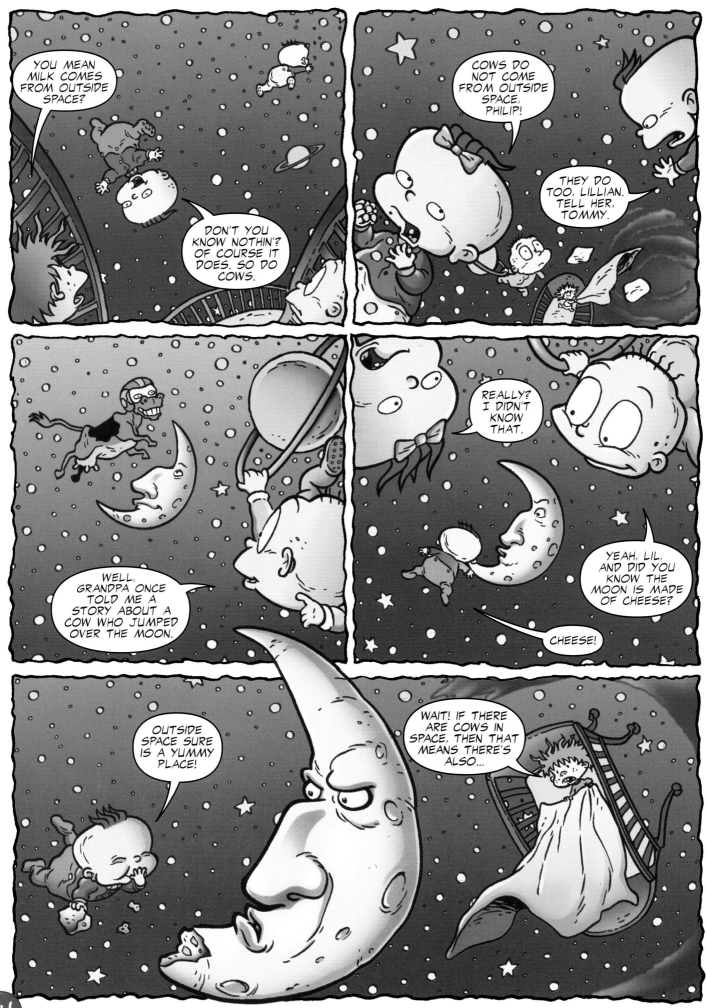

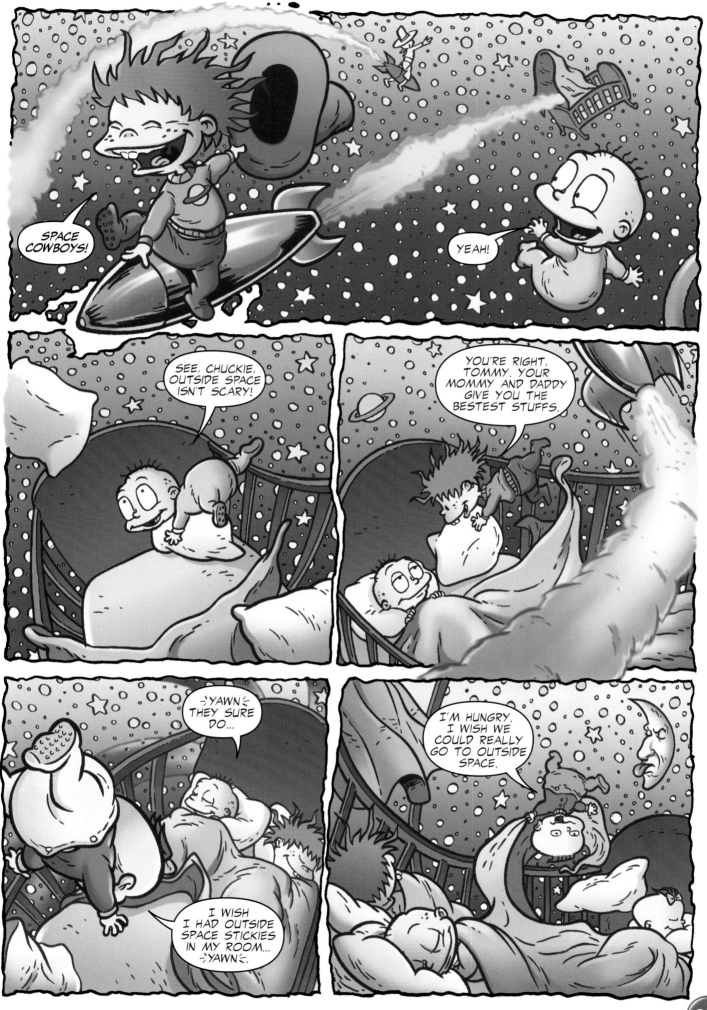

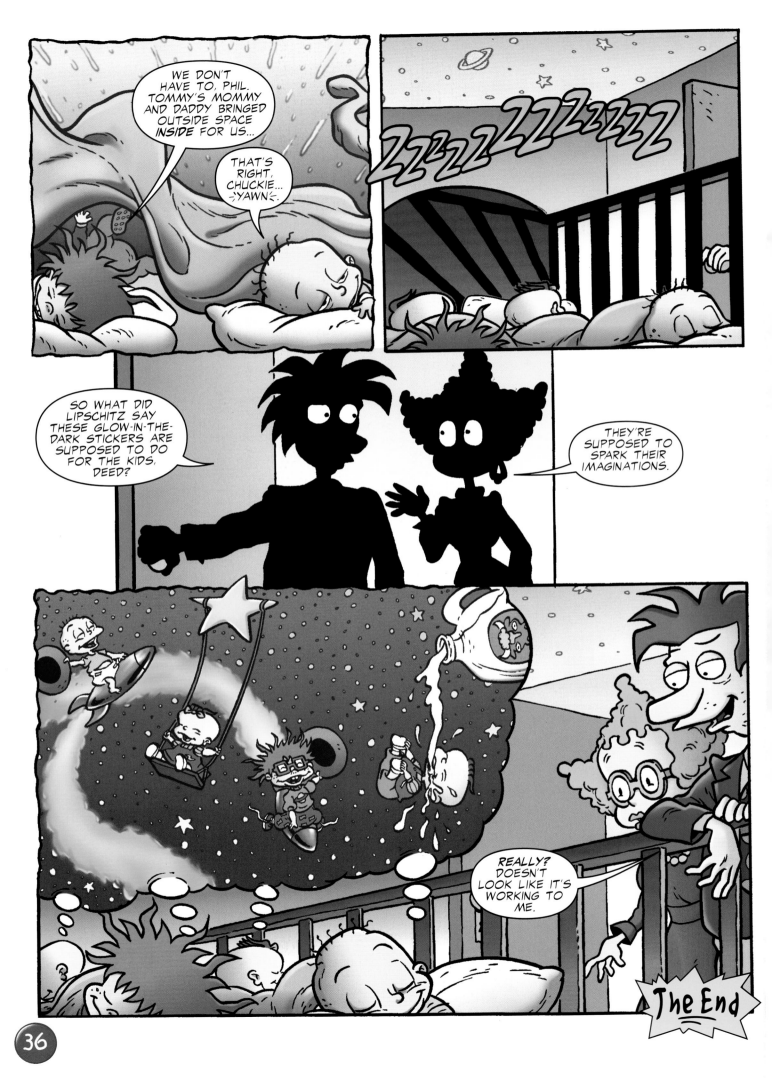

NAME GAME

Follow the letters to spell three Rugrats names — Tommy, Phil and Suzie. The names will lead you to Angelica

Answer: page 61

PAIR UP

A

B

Look carefully at
these five pictures
of Chuckie.

Which two
pictures are exactly
the same?

C

and

are the same

D

Answers: page 60

E

TWIN SISTER ACT

COLOUR BY SHAPE

USE THE KEY BELOW TO COLOUR UP THE PALS.

■ = Orange ✱ = Green ● = Red

◆ = Blue ▲ = Purple

Answers: page 60

HAIR RAISING!

Who's behind the wall? Draw a line matching the Rugrats' names to the right hair.

Chuckie   Dil   Kimi   Tommy

Answers: page 61

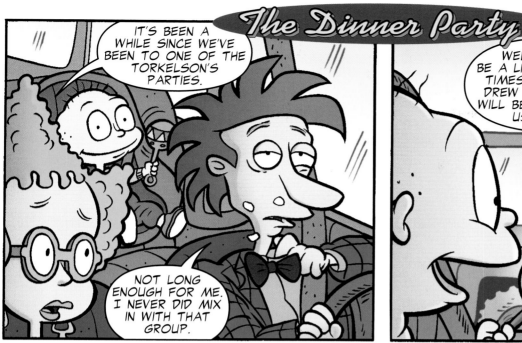

IT'S BEEN A WHILE SINCE WE'VE BEEN TO ONE OF THE TORKELSON'S PARTIES.

NOT LONG ENOUGH FOR ME. I NEVER DID MIX IN WITH THAT GROUP.

WELL, THEY CAN BE A LITTLE SNOOTY AT TIMES. BUT AT LEAST DREW AND CHARLOTTE WILL BE THERE TO KEEP US COMPANY.

HEY, ANGELICA, IT'S ME, TOMMY!

SOME BABIES ARE AMUSED BY THE DUMBEST THINGS.

HEY, ANGELICA! HI!

HUH?

HEY, DADDY, LOOK AT THAT TRUCK!

HEY, MISTER TRUCK DRIVER! HONK YOUR HORN!

HONK!

54

57

COLOUR ME

Colour in this picture of Tommy on his Skateboard!

ANSWERS

PAIR UP

Look carefully at these five pictures of Chuckie.

Which two pictures are exactly the same?

B and C are the same

COLOUR BY SHAPE

USE THE KEY BELOW TO COLOUR UP THE PALS.

■ = Orange   ✱ = Green   ● = Red
◆ = Blue   ▲ = Purple

WHOSE SHADOW?

Can you guess who this is? Colour in the areas containing one circle and find out! If you don't recognize the shadow, unscramble the letters to work out this Rugrat's name.

ANGELICA

HANG ON to your diaper!

Tommy is giving Dil a piggy back ride. Help him find his way through the maze to Spike.

OH DIL!!

Can you spot the five differences between these two pictures?

HAIR RAISING!

Who's behind the wall? Draw a line matching the Rugrats' names to the right hair.

Chuckie   Dill   Kimi   Tommy

SPOT THE BALL

Tommy, Chuckie and Phil are each playing with a football.

REPTAR'S Code Breaker

Put the initial letters of each person into the answer grid to spell out the message.

Some letters are done for you.

What is Reptar saying?

	E				
	E		U		E	

Write you answer here

R E P T A R   R U L E S

NAME GAME

Follow the letters to spell 3 Rugrats names.
The names will lead you to Angelica

SPIKE'S WORDSEARCH

Can you help Spike find his favourite words in the puzzle?

Tick off the word from the list when you have found it.

Dog ☐
Bones ☐
Lead ☐
Walk ☐
Dig ☐
Bury ☐
Kennel ☐
Collar ☐
Stick ☐
Tail ☐
Wag ☐
Bark ☐
Spike ☐

C	E	M	Z	C	O	L	L	A	R
C	J	T	Q	G	O	K	D	M	Z
E	W	K	V	J	A	E	C	D	H
T	A	I	L	N	L	W	H	D	E
B	A	R	K	D	M	N	F	S	I
N	S	X	B	O	N	E	S	T	J
B	U	R	Y	G	E	L	X	I	P
W	A	L	K	P	F	L	J	C	S
S	N	X	J	D	A	E	L	H	I
Y	H	S	G	G	A	W	D	I	G

SNOW RACE

Who is going to Win the Race to the Snowman?

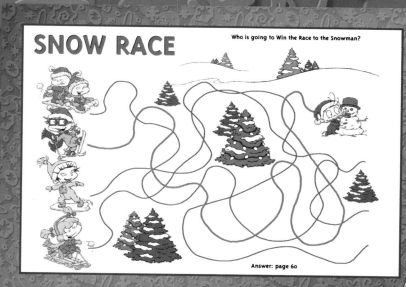

Answer: page 60

61